A Penny-Farthing Press, Inc. Book

penny
farthing
press™

Decoy: Menagerie, Part 1
Published by Penny-Farthing Press, Inc.
10370 Richmond Avenue, Suite 980
Houston, Texas 77042
(713) 780-0300 or (800) 926-2669
corp@pfpress.com
www.pfpress.com

987654321

ISBN: 09719012-3-6
First Printing: April 2005

Printed in Korea

DECOY™:

CREATED by
COURTNEY HUDDLESTON

PART 1

COVER DESIGNED by
ANDRÉ McBRIDE

Penny-Farthing Press, Inc.

Publisher
Ken White, Jr.

Editor-in-Chief
Marlaine Maddux

Creative Director
Trainor Houghton

Art Director
Charles M. Hancock

Senior Editor
Michelle Harman

Talent Coordinator
Courtney Huddleston

Graphic Designer
André McBride

Vice President of Marketing
and Media Communications
Pamela Miltenberger

Office Manager
Pam Johnston

Accounts Manager
Selma Medina

Table of Contents

FOREWORD

Creating *Decoy* wasn't a sudden brainstorm, and I didn't receive inspiration from a muse or divine visitation. I also didn't become an artist or a success overnight as so many young, up-and-coming talents hope. My *Decoy* and artistic journeys have been life-long travels through a broken arm, a restless imagination, five hundred rejection letters, and the births of my beautiful daughters, Courtney Jr., and Phoenix.

When I broke my arm in the seventh grade, I was unable to play football (an adolescent boy's surefire ticket to acceptance in junior high). To pass the time, I took pencil in hand and began drawing Transformers while everyone else practiced football. I found that I enjoyed that time, and even after the arm healed, ideas began to creep into my head about fierce, seemingly adorable beings and massive beasts that held compassion beneath their grotesque exteriors.

I thought a story about a race of cute aliens that used aggression, violence, and shape-shifting abilities to conquer planets and spread death throughout the universe would be a cool adventure and a twist on stereotyping. In high school, this dangerous alien race took on a name: the Metas. A homeworld was born soon after in the planet Nacrum, and the Metas filled this place and my mind with numerous possibilities. Born green and innocent, the Metas have to commit acts of violence in order to determine their adult color and caste alliance. Genetically predetermined as Red Warriors, Yellow Scientists, Blue Navigators, or Orange Builders, all Metalings must pass their initiation to discover their position in Meta society. A mysterious sixth color class–the Purple Telepaths–is also possible, but this strain is so rare that the Meta culture regards it as a myth.

So I had my villains, but I still needed a weakness for the indestructible aliens I had created. The Achilles' heel came in the guise of my original idea of the compassionate monster. With their thick, lizard-like skin, the Kranch can withstand a Meta attack long enough to puncture the shape-shifting skin with a venomous tail spike. The poison renders a Meta unable to maintain shape and leads to a prolonged, painful death. Although the Kranch are threats to the Metas, I didn't want them to share the same rage. Whereas the Metas want to rid the universe of all Kranch, the Kranch are a gentle race that prefers peace to violence, and only fight when provoked or when protecting other alien species.

With this story imagined, I decided to take a piece of that world in my imagination and throw in Earth and a known reality to see what would happen. The result was a kind-hearted, green Meta whose refusal to partake in ritual aggression resulted in his banishment from Nacrum. I had a lot of fun imagining how this child-like alien would interact with Earth creatures, and as he related to each individual animal, I thought of the perfect name: Decoy. As a shape-shifter, this Meta could imitate anything he chose in an effort to learn about a new culture.

I also wanted to show the lengths to which my hero would rebel against his ancestry, and I found the perfect example in his first meeting with a Human. As a headstrong, ambitious rookie police officer, Bobby Luck is, in many ways, an extension of Decoy's character. Both are young, naïve, and unaware of a great deal of the injustice and evil in the universe. As a result of this ignorance, Luck eventually gets himself hurt. In an act of ultimate sacrifice, Decoy finds the mortally wounded rookie and offers himself in a symbiotic merging to save the Earthling's life. The rest, as they say, is history. Unable to survive without the other, Decoy and Bobby Luck travel the city fighting crime, discovering the good and bad sides of Humanity, and playing pranks on one another.

I find that as I grow older, the *Decoy* story reflects what I've seen along my way in life. The story of unassuming characters taking on a world bigger than themselves, never forgetting the punch line is really the philosophy I try to live. Sometimes, though, I find myself revisiting the same missteps over and over again. I think the main thing I've taken from my time with *Decoy* is the ability to regain a sense of humor and creativity at all times.

As you read this book, I hope that you'll develop your own talent and create fictional worlds where anything is possible. The most important thing to keep in mind, however, is to draw on life experience (no pun intended) and make yourself happy doing it.

Now, with that out of the way, please proceed with *Decoy: Menagerie*, Part 1.

Courtney Huddleston

A WORD FROM BOBBY AND DECOY.

Hello, My name is Bobby Luck. What you just saw wasn't me bragging or showing off. It was just an opportunity to give you a taste of what's to come in the following pages. By the end of this journey, I'm hoping you'll have a better understanding of who I am, and what my relationship with Decoy is like. And, just in case you're new, and wondering who Decoy is, he's the little green alien looking over my right shoulder. Good. Now with that out of the way, let the fun begin.

The Answer

Story: M.
   Dedicated to Jean B. Nichols (1942-2005)
Pencils: Rove
Colors: Mike Garcia
Letters: Ed Dukeshire

THE PLANET NACRUM.
THREE-HUNDRED YEARS AGO.

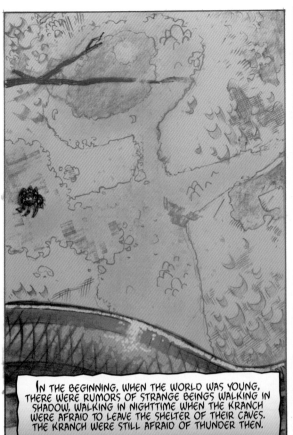

IN THE BEGINNING, WHEN THE WORLD WAS YOUNG, THERE WERE RUMORS OF STRANGE BEINGS WALKING IN SHADOW, WALKING IN NIGHTTIME WHEN THE KRANCH WERE AFRAID TO LEAVE THE SHELTER OF THEIR CAVES. THE KRANCH WERE STILL AFRAID OF THUNDER THEN.

THEY WERE AFRAID OF THE STORMS THAT DEVELOPED SUDDENLY AS IF THE WORLD'S OUTER LAYER WAS ON FIRE. AND SOMETIMES THE SKY'S GROWL AND FLASHES WERE SO GREAT THAT ODD...THINGS FELL FROM THE SKY.

THESE THINGS WERE STRANGE. CERTAINLY NO KRANCH POSSESSED THE POWER TO CREATE SUCH ITEMS. NO KRANCH HAD EVER SEEN ANYTHING SO MAGICAL. SO THE KRANCH PUT THE THINGS ON HIGH PLACES FOR ALL KRANCH TO SEE, FOR ALL KRANCH TO KNOW THAT THERE WAS SOMETHING OUT THERE.

THE EARLY KRANCH TRIBE SPLIT FIRST INTO TWO AND THEN FOUR GROUPS THAT WALKED INTO THE WORLD WHERE KRANCH HAD NEVER BEEN BEFORE. THEY SAW NEW CREATURES, NEW LANDS, AND ALWAYS THEY SAW THINGS IN THE SHADOWS...WATCHING.

THE SOUTHERN, TRIBE BUILT TOWERS TO CALL THE STRANGE BEINGS OUT INTO THE OPEN AND THE TOWERS GREW LARGER AND MORE INTRICATE OVER THE CENTURIES.

THE NORTHERN TRIBE LEARNED TO HARNESS THE COLD WEATHER OF THE NACRUM SUMMER TO ITS ADVANTAGE. THEY LEARNED TO CONSERVE THEIR FOOD WITH ICE. THEY LEARNED THE LANGUAGES OF THE OTHER CREATURES AND SANG SONGS OF THE STRANGE BEINGS.

IN THE EAST, THE TRIBE BUILT MIRACULOUS VEHICLES TO CHALLENGE THE TWELVE OCEANS. THEY LEARNED WAYS TO NAVIGATE USING THE OBJECTS THEY SAW IN THE NIGHT SKY IN ORDER TO SEARCH OUT THE HOMELAND OF THE BEINGS.

AND THE WESTERN TRIBE SET THE KRANCH LANGUAGE ONTO ROCK TABLETS. THEY STUDIED THE THINGS THAT FELL FROM THE SKY AND PONDERED WHAT MANNER OF CREATURE THE BEINGS WERE. THEY RECORDED THEIR OBSERVATIONS.

THEN ONE DAY, THE PLANET SHOOK FROM THE FORCE OF A STORM WORSE THAN ANY STORM THE KRANCH HAD EVER SEEN. THE KRANCH WERE AFRAID OF THUNDER AGAIN. THEY COWERED IN THEIR DWELLINGS AND UNDER THEIR TOWERS. THEY WROTE ABOUT THE STORM AND SET OUT IN THEIR VEHICLES TO FIND THE SOURCE.

BUT THEY DIDN'T LOOK FAR. THE SOURCE CAME TO THEM. THOUSANDS OF THE BEINGS SET OUT INTO THE WORLD. THEY OFFERED STRANGE THINGS TO THE KRANCH AND INVITED THEM TO SEE THE THINGS THAT HAD CAUSED THE STORMS, STRANGE HOUSE-LIKE ITEMS THE BEINGS USED TO PIERCE THE OUTER LAYER OF NACRUM.

THE BEINGS WERE CALLED META AND THEY WERE RULED BY A SOLITARY, RARE PURPLE.

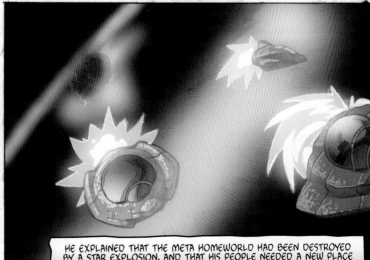

HE EXPLAINED THAT THE META HOMEWORLD HAD BEEN DESTROYED BY A STAR EXPLOSION, AND THAT HIS PEOPLE NEEDED A NEW PLACE TO LIVE. HE EXPLAINED THAT THE META HAD BEEN WATCHING THE KRANCH FOR THE RIGHT MOMENT TO MAKE A FORMAL INTRODUCTION.

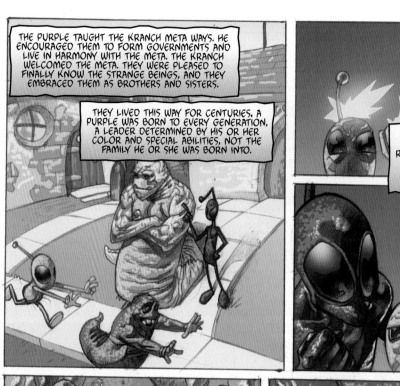

THE PURPLE TAUGHT THE KRANCH META WAYS. HE ENCOURAGED THEM TO FORM GOVERNMENTS AND LIVE IN HARMONY WITH THE META. THE KRANCH WELCOMED THE META. THEY WERE PLEASED TO FINALLY KNOW THE STRANGE BEINGS, AND THEY EMBRACED THEM AS BROTHERS AND SISTERS.

THEY LIVED THIS WAY FOR CENTURIES. A PURPLE WAS BORN TO EVERY GENERATION, A LEADER DETERMINED BY HIS OR HER COLOR AND SPECIAL ABILITIES, NOT THE FAMILY HE OR SHE WAS BORN INTO.

THE META HAD NO CONCEPTS OF RICH AND POOR, BUT THE PURPLE'S RANDOM GENETIC CREATION INSURED THAT DYNASTIES COULD NOT BE FORMED. RULING FAMILIES COULD NOT BE ESTABLISHED.

NO ONE KNEW WHEN, WHERE, AND WHO WOULD PRODUCE THE NEXT PURPLE. IT JUST HAPPENED.

THE PURPLE RULED WITH A LEADER ELECTED BY THE KRANCH.

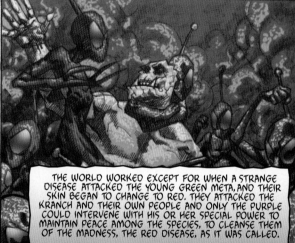

THE WORLD WORKED EXCEPT FOR WHEN A STRANGE DISEASE ATTACKED THE YOUNG GREEN META, AND THEIR SKIN BEGAN TO CHANGE TO RED. THEY ATTACKED THE KRANCH AND THEIR OWN PEOPLE AND ONLY THE PURPLE COULD INTERVENE WITH HIS OR HER SPECIAL POWER TO MAINTAIN PEACE AMONG THE SPECIES, TO CLEANSE THEM OF THE MADNESS, THE RED DISEASE, AS IT WAS CALLED.

THE PURPLE'S MAIN DUTY WAS NOT TO LORD OVER THE META, BUT TO KEEP THEM SAFE AND HAPPY.

META MYTHS WARNED OF A TIME WHEN THE RED DISEASE THREATENED TO DESTROY THE ENTIRE META SPECIES. A PURPLE WAS BORN, UNLIKE ANY OTHER META THE SPECIES HAD SEEN--TO COMBAT THE DISEASE. THE META SANG SONGS ABOUT THIS BEING. THE FIRST PURPLE. THE ONE THAT WARNED THAT A DAY WOULD COME WHEN THE PURPLE MIGHT NOT BE ABLE TO STOP THE DISEASE, WHEN THE META PEOPLE WOULD BE PLUNGED INTO CHAOS AND VIOLENCE. THE META STROVE TO AVOID THAT DAY. THEY ACTUALLY FOUGHT AGAINST THE DISEASE AS MUCH AS THEY COULD.

CHAOS IS SET INTO MOTION BY LITTLE THINGS.

EVEN A DAY SHARED WITH BELOVED COMPANIONS, CAN TURN DISASTROUS...

...WHEN PLAY GETS TOO ROUGH.

WHEN SOMEONE GETS HURT.

TO THE SHOCK OF HIS COMPANIONS, THE METALING LOST HIS SHAPE.

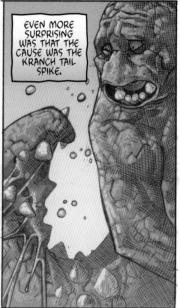

EVEN MORE SURPRISING WAS THAT THE CAUSE WAS THE KRANCH TAIL SPIKE.

THEY WATCHED-- META AND KRANCH-- AS THEIR FRIEND DIED.

AND AS THE KRANCH WEPT, SOMETHING BEGAN TO BUBBLE IN THE META'S BRAIN.

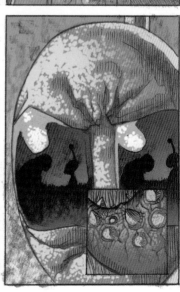

THAT SOMETHING TOOK THE FORM OF A CHEMICAL CHANGE, A CHANGE THAT AWAKENED THE RED DISEASE LYING DORMANT IN THE YOUNG ONE'S BODY.

AND HE KNEW AT THAT MOMENT AS RAGE COURSED THROUGH HIS VEINS THAT VIOLENCE CAUSED THE TRANSFORMATION.

HE ALSO KNEW HOW TO KILL METAS.

AND DURING THE WORST EPIDEMIC OF THE RED DISEASE, SUCH A DISCOVERY CAME ALONG AT THE WORST POSSIBLE TIME.

THE PURPLE, AS THE MOST POWERFUL META, HELD THE RESPONSIBILITY OF DISPELLING RIOTS WITH HIS UNIQUE POWER.

THE KRANCH LEADER, ELECTED AND RECOGNIZED AS THE WISEST KRANCH ON THE PLANET, HELD THE RESPONSIBILITY OF MAINTAINING PEACE.

THEY SET OUT TO END THE EPIDEMIC AND BLOODSHED...

...AS PEACEFULLY AS POSSIBLE.

THEY WORKED TOGETHER...

...THE PURPLE WITH HIS PSYCHIC ABILITY...

...THE KRANCH WITH HIS STRENGTH.

WHEN THEY WERE SURROUNDED...

...THE KRANCH HELD BACK THE LEADERS...

...AS THE PURPLE BEGAN THE CLEANSING PROCESS.

HE WASHED THROUGH THE
RED HORDE, PAST THE CITY
AND INTO THE DESERT.

THE RED DISEASE
WAS FLUSHED FROM
THE BODIES OF HIS
FOLLOWERS, THE
BODIES ON THE
GROUND...

...SAVE FOR ONE.

THE ONE WHO KNEW THE BATTLE WAS NOT DONE.

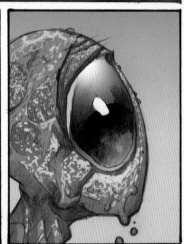

THE YOUNG ONE CLAIMED FEAR.

AND THE PURPLE, WITH NO REASON TO SUSPECT OTHERWISE...

...OBLIGED HIM...

...BROUGHT HIM NEAR...

...COMFORTED HIM.

BUT HE NOTICED THE RED EYES TOO LATE.

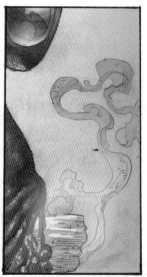

BUT THE PURPLE WAS LIKE NO OTHER META.

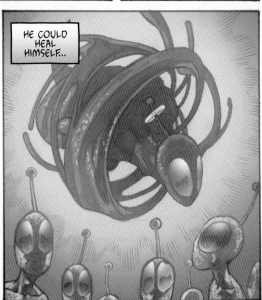

HE COULD HEAL HIMSELF...

...STOP THE KRANCH SPIKE'S TOXIC EFFECT.

BUT THE YOUNG ONE HAD A PLAN.

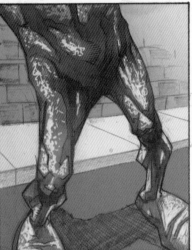

HE SHOWED THE OTHER META HIS POWER.

HE SHOWED THEM HIS KNOWLEDGE.

IN THAT INSTANT, HE CHANGED NACRUM CIVILIZATION FOREVER.

AS THE GREENS TRANSFORMED, THEY BECAME RED, BLUE, YELLOW, AND ORANGE.

THEY WERE NO LONGER EQUAL.

THEY WERE NO LONGER INNOCENT.

IF THEY PERCEIVED A THREAT...

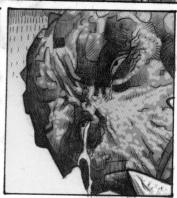

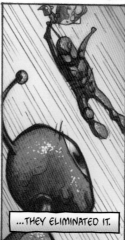

...THEY ELIMINATED IT.

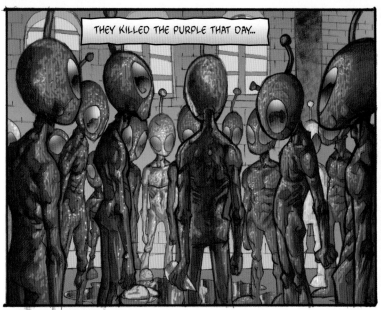

THEY KILLED THE PURPLE THAT DAY...

...AND FULFILLED THE FIRST PURPLE'S PROPHECY.

THE CHAOS THAT BEFELL THE META WAS MORE HORRIBLE THAN IMAGINED.

THEY WOULD KILL ALL PURPLES AT BIRTH AFTER THAT, UNTIL THERE WERE NO MORE.

THEY LOST ALL RESPECT FOR LIFE...

...AND ALL RESPECT FOR US.

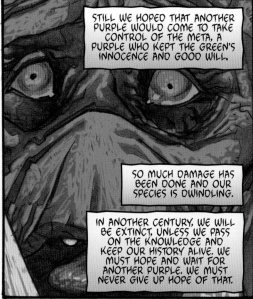

STILL WE HOPED THAT ANOTHER PURPLE WOULD COME TO TAKE CONTROL OF THE META, A PURPLE WHO KEPT THE GREEN'S INNOCENCE AND GOOD WILL.

SO MUCH DAMAGE HAS BEEN DONE AND OUR SPECIES IS DWINDLING.

IN ANOTHER CENTURY, WE WILL BE EXTINCT, UNLESS WE PASS ON THE KNOWLEDGE AND KEEP OUR HISTORY ALIVE. WE MUST HOPE AND WAIT FOR ANOTHER PURPLE. WE MUST NEVER GIVE UP HOPE OF THAT.

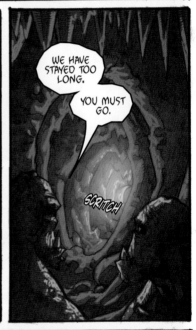

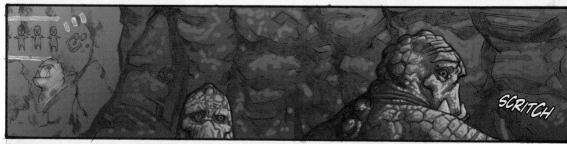

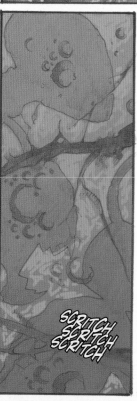

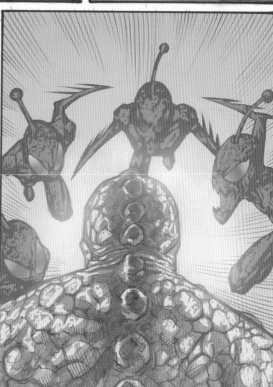

WE MUST HOPE AND WAIT FOR ANOTHER PURPLE.
WE MUST NEVER GIVE UP HOPE OF THAT.

THE END.

Hard-Boiled Private Eye Guy

Writer: Azad Injejikian
Pencils: Sean Galloway
Layouts: Jonboy Meyers
Inks: James Taylor
Colors: Mike Garcia
Letters: Ed Dukeshire

THE STINK FROM THE CITY SEWERS THAT CREPT IN THROUGH THE OPEN WINDOW IN MY OFFICE TONIGHT COULD MAKE A PARMESAN CHEESE HOLD ITS NOSE. BETWEEN THAT AND CUTTING THIS MONTH'S ALIMONY CHECK TO MY EX-WIFE, TODAY IS TURNING OUT TO BE ANOTHER STELLAR DAY.

NOTE THE SARCASM, FOLKS.

BUT IT'S GETTING BETTER.

THE NAME'S LUCK. BOBBY LUCK. I'M WHAT YOU'D CALL AN OL' FASHIONED GUMSHOE... AND RIGHT NOW, I'M STARING AT THE HOTTEST SKIRT TO EVER SET FOOT IN MY OFFICE.

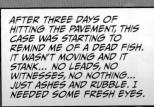

AFTER THREE DAYS OF HITTING THE PAVEMENT, THIS CASE WAS STARTING TO REMIND ME OF A DEAD FISH. IT WASN'T MOVING AND IT STANK... NO LEADS, NO WITNESSES, NO NOTHING... JUST ASHES AND RUBBLE. I NEEDED SOME FRESH EYES.

THE FELLA GOES BY THE NAME DECOY.

DEE-COY. SOUNDS FRENCH TO ME.

WELL, WHEREVER HE'S FROM, HE'S ONE OF THE FEW PRIVATE EYES IN DOLPHIN CITY WHO ISN'T ON THE PAYROLL OF SOME CAPPO. HE CAME HIGHLY RECOMMENDED, AND WITH GOOD REASON.

HE'S GOT A BAG OF TRICKS THAT'D MAKE THE REST OF US LOOK LIKE WE'RE HOLDIN' PURSES!

THE KID IS GOOD. HOW GOOD YOU ASK?

YOU KNOW THE SAYING "HARDER TO FIND THAN A NEEDLE IN A HAYSTACK"?

WELL, HE ONCE FOUND THE NEEDLE!

DECOY...
FRENCH DETECTIVE
EXTRAORDINAIRE!

...GASOLINE!

OR SO IT SEEMED.... I'LL TAKE A SAMPLE WITH ME TO HAVE A FRIEND ANALYZE.

LOOKS LIKE A SIZE TEN TO ME. BUT SOMETHING IS DIFFERENT.

THE SHAPE IS NARROWER....

CONVENIENT ESCAPE ROUTE IF YOU ASK ME. WHOEVER DID THIS KNEW THE AREA. SOMEONE LOCAL IS IN ON THIS... TIME TO VISIT AN OLD FRIEND.

THE LEFT HOOK. MY OLD HAUNT FROM BACK IN MY BOXING DAYS. THE PLACE IS RUN BY MY OLD PROMOTER, BIG DADDY LEVIN. HE'S A CONNECTED GUY IN THIS PART OF TOWN. IF SOMETHING LIKE A BUILDING GETTING TORCHED TAKES PLACE, HE'D KNOW ABOUT IT. I WOULDA GONE TO HIM SOONER, BUT I PROMISED MYSELF THAT I WOULDN'T STEP FOOT BACK IN HERE UNLESS IT WAS ABSOLUTELY NECESSARY OR WITH SOME SERIOUS MUSCLE BY MY SIDE.

THE MUSCLE IN THIS CASE IS MY LITTLE FRENCH FRIEND.

IT'S THE FIRST TIME I'VE BEEN BACK SINCE GOING LEGIT. I'M NOT EXPECTING A WARM RECEPTION.

KNOCK KNOCK

SNACT!

YOUS!

HEY LITTLE MO... BIG LEVIN IN TONIGHT?

NOTS TO SEES YOUS. BIG LEVINS WANTS NOTHINGS TO DO WITH YOUS ANYMORES AND YOUS KNOWS IT.

SO WHYS DON'T YOUS BEATS IT, BEFORE YOUS ENDS UP EATING PAVEMENTS.

LISTEN... LETS DISCUSS THIS--

DON'T MAKES ME HAFTAS OPENS THIS DOOR, LUCKS!

LOOK, MO...I DON'T WANT TO HURT YOU--

HAHAHA!-- YOUS?

HOWS EXACTLY DO YOUS PLANS ON DOINGS THAT, SEEINGS HOWS I'MS IN HERES, AND YOURS ARE OUT 'DERES?

DECOY....

CHAPTER THREE: CONNECTING THE DOTS

LEVIN'S ADMISSION LEFT ME WITH A SICK FEELING IN MY STOMACH. AT FIRST, I QUESTIONED WHETHER HE WAS JUST TRYING TO SCREW WITH MY HEAD... BUT A FEW QUICK INQUIRIES CONFIRMED HIS ACCUSATIONS. TIME TO BREAK THE BAD NEWS TO THE ICE PRINCESS.

EVENIN'... I'M HERE TO SEE MRS. MORENO, PLEASE.

OH, YOU CANNOT BE SERIOUS....

IT'S OKAY... HE'S WITH ME, GERARD.

VERY WELL, MADAME.

MR. FANCYPANTS DOESN'T REALIZE HOW CLOSE HE CAME TO DRINKING THROUGH A STRAW FOR THE NEXT 2 WEEKS. THE ICE PRINCESS JUST SAVED HIS REAR.

AS YOU CAN PROBABLY SEE, THIS ISN'T A GOOD TIME, MR. LUCKY. THIS BETTER BE IMPORTANT.

YOU BET... I JUST NEED TO CORROBORATE A FEW DETAILS...

...AND IT'S *LUCK*, NOT LUCKY!

LET'S TAKE THIS SOMEWHERE WHERE WE WON'T BE INTERRUPTED.

...YOUR SISTER IS THE ONE WHO BURNED DOWN YOUR LITTLE PILATES PET PROJECT.

ARE YOU INSANE, DETECTIVE LUCK?

SHARP AS A TACK, MRS. MORENO, I ASSURE YOU.

I DID A LITTLE DIGGING AND FOUND SOME INTERESTING FACTS.

TESSA'S WASN'T THE FIRST PILATES HEALTH CENTER TO GO DOWN IN FLAMES. A TOTAL OF THREE PILATES ESTABLISHMENTS IN DOLPHIN CITY HAD FALLEN VICTIM TO SOME MISFORTUNE OR ANOTHER.

-=GASP=-

SOMEONE NEEDED THOSE CLUBS TO GO DOWN. SOMEONE WITH SOMETHING TO LOSE. I BELIEVE IT WAS ALICE MORENO WHO SET THAT FIRE!

IN THE LATE 80'S, A HEALTH CRAZE CALLED JAZZERCIZE HIT DOLPHIN CITY LIKE A TON OF BRICKS. YOU COULDN'T TURN A CORNER WITHOUT SEEING WOMEN AND MEN, OLD AND YOUNG ADORNED, IN LEG WARMERS, SPANDEX, AND BANDANAS.

BUT BY THE EARLY NINETIES, JAZZERCIZE WAS KILLED OFF BY A NEW CRAZE: YOGA.

A YOUNG ALICE MORENO SET UP HER OWN YOGA CLASS WHICH BECAME THE ENVY OF ALL HEALTH CLUBS IN DOLPHIN CITY. ALMOST SINGLE HANDEDLY, SHE KILLED OFF THE JAZZERCIZE CRAZE, GREW IN SOCIAL STATUS, AND REIGNED AS THE HEALTH QUEEN OF DOLPHIN CITY FOR A DECADE...

...UNTIL RECENTLY.

MUCH LIKE THE JAZZERCIZE CRAZE ALICE AND HER CONTEMPORARIES KILLED OFF, YOGA CLASSES ARE SLOWLY DYING OFF IN EVERY PART OF THE COUNTRY, BEING REPLACED OR TAKEN OVER BY PILATES CLASSES. THE NEW OPIUM FOR THE MASSES. ALICE RECOGNIZED THIS, AND HAD TO TAKE ACTION!

Single Inebriated Operating Plan

STORY: Arvid Nelson
PENCILS: Fernando Alejandrez
INKS: James Taylor
COLORS: Mike Garcia
LETTERS: Ed Dukeshire

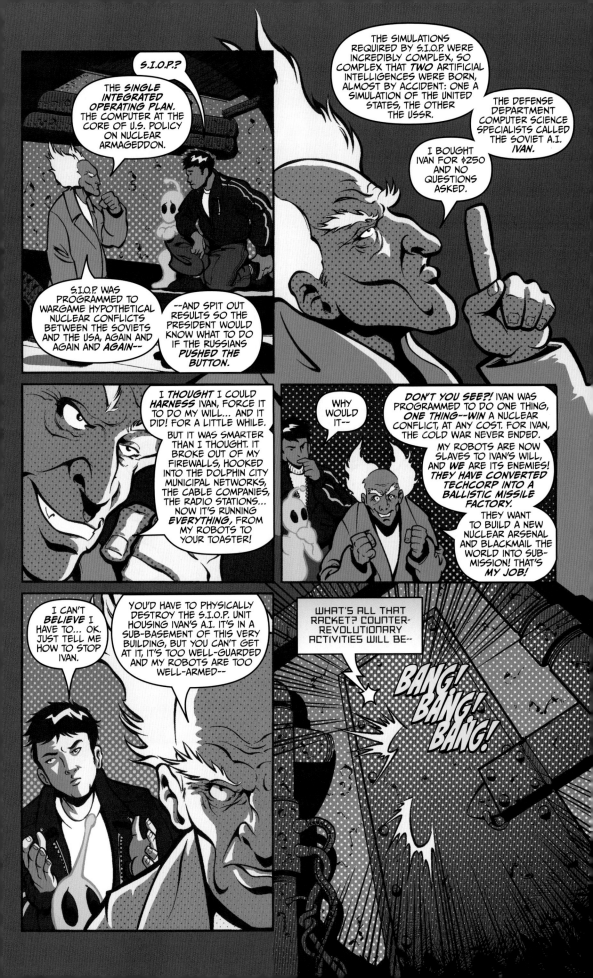

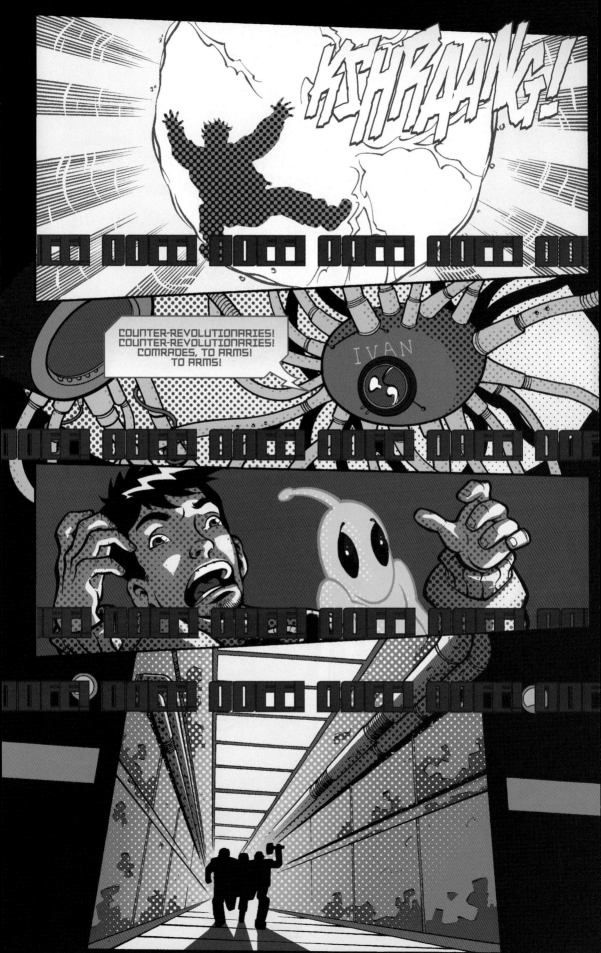

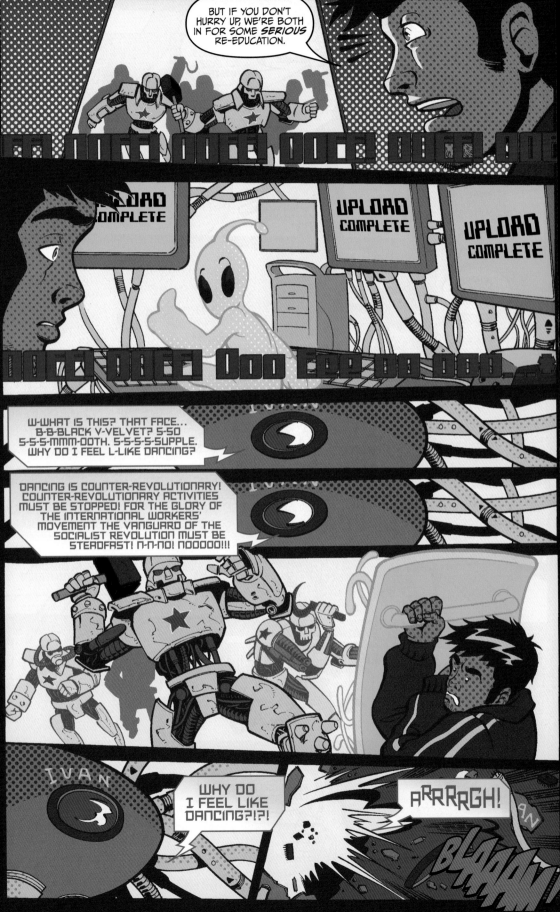

THE END.

Going Through A Stage

Story: Ty Templeton
Pencils: Ryan Woodward
Inks: James Taylor
Colors: Mike Garcia
Letters: Ed Dukeshire

I'D SPENT MY ROOKIE YEAR TRYING TO RAISE CAPTAIN TANNER'S LOW OPINION OF ME. LATER THAT NIGHT I FIGURED I HAD ANOTHER CHANCE TO DO *JUST* THAT.

♪ YOU LEFT ME, LEFT ME, LEFT ME, LEFT ME, **LEFT ME, LEAVE ME, TAKE ME, CLEAVE ME.** NO ROMANCE, NO ROMANCE FOR SUCH A LITTLE LANCE, NOW TELL ME HOW YOU SLEEP. ♪

♪ TELL ME ♪ **HOW YOU SLEEP!!**

IT MAY NOT BE THE BEST MUSIC MY PLANET HAS TO OFFER, DECOY, BUT THERE'S NOTHING TO BE *AFRAID* OF.

THAT'S DECOY, MY SECRET ALIEN PARTNER. EVERY COP SHOULD HAVE ONE.

WE MET A YEAR AGO WHEN DECOY SAVED MY LIFE FROM A GUN SHOT WOUND WITH HIS ALIEN POWERS. HE'S BEEN AT MY SIDE AND INSIDE MY SKIN EVER SINCE.

ANTICIPATION? OF WHAT? NOTHING HAPPENS AFTER THIS, BUT *MORE* SINGING. IT'S JUST *FUN*--

SACRIFICE?

OH! NO. THERE WON'T BE ONE.

WE DON'T *DO* RITUAL SACRIFICE ON THIS PLANET ANYMORE.

EXCEPT ON COURT TV.

TWO HOURS OF EAR TORTURE EVENTUALLY ENDED. BUT DECOY LOVED IT, AND I DIDN'T WANT TO RUIN HIS FIRST EARTH CONCERT.

WOOO! WOOO?

NOTHING WRONG WITH DANCING. YOU'RE *SUPPOSED* TO JUST *GO* WITH THE MUSIC. THAT'S THE WHOLE POINT--

GET OFF ME! SECURITY! *SECURITY!!*

I DIDN'T NOTICE WHAT I'D JUST SAID.

BECAUSE SOMEONE HAD OPENED THE **WRONG** DOOR BACKSTAGE, AND A **HERD** OF FANS HAD GOTTEN INTO THE WRONG HALL.

IT'S HER!!

HEY LANA!!

STOP!

LOVE!

ALLANAH!

AND I HAD TO DO SOMETHING ABOUT IT.

AS FAST AS THOUGHT, DECOY LIVED UP TO HIS NAME AND DISTRACTED THE CROWD WHILE I LOOKED FOR A FORTIFIED DOOR TO HOLD OFF A SIEGE.

MY CHOICE OF DOORS WAS THE **NEXT** MISTAKE I MADE THAT NIGHT.

THIS WAY! QUICK!

NICE HORDE SCARING, DECOY. SEVERAL POINTS AWARDED.

I THINK WE'VE JUST SAVED ALLANAH LOVE FROM SERIOUS INJURY.

I OUGHT TO GET A MEDAL OR SOMETHING.

THUMP!

THAT WAS MY BRIEF MOMENT OF TRIUMPH. WHEN I THOUGHT I'D DONE SOMETHING RIGHT.

BUT THAT FEELING OF WELL BEING WAS ANOTHER MISTAKE.

OH *NO!*

NO!
NO NO NO!

DRUNK-OR-WORSE LOVE HAD PULLED MOST OF THE ROOM OVER ONTO HERSELF.

DAMN IT!
DAMN IT!
DAMN IT!
DAMN IT!

YOU *TOLD* ME THIS WAS GOING TO HAPPEN? *WHEN?*

UNFORTUNATELY DECOY MISINTERPRETED THE SITUATION.

THIS WAS *NOT* A HUNT. IT WAS AN ACCIDENT.

SHE'S *NOT* PREY, IT WAS JUST *FANS...* NOW QUIET, DECOY, I HAVE TO RADIO FOR AN AMBULANCE.

BUT ALLANAH LOVE WOULDN'T NEED AN AMBULANCE.

NOT WITH THE CURE TO ALL HER INJURIES RIGHT IN THE ROOM.

WHAT THE...?

BLEEDING OUT FROM A 45 MM HOLE IN MY CHEST.

AND, LITERALLY, FROM OUT OF THE SKY, MY SAVIOUR CAME AND PHYSICALLY ENTERED MY WOUND--

--MY BODY, MY LIFE.

JUST LIKE I WATCHED HIM DO FOR ALLANAH LOVE JUST NOW.

AND EVERY MOMENT OF TERROR AND CONFUSION THAT I FELT A YEAR AGO ON THE GROUND IN THE FOREST--

WAIT! YOU CAN'T GO!

--CAME RUSHING BACK AS I WATCHED DECOY LEAVE WITH SOMEONE ELSE.

I TOLD YOU TO BACK OFF, SECURITY MAN! TOBY, HOTEL NOW!

YOU HAVE TO STAY. WE CAN'T BE SEPARATED! YOU DON'T UNDERSTAND!

I THINK YOU DON'T UNDERSTAND.

I DON'T WANT TROUBLE WITH COPS, AND YOU DON'T WANT TROUBLE WITH ME.

BUT....

WE CAN'T BE SEPARATED-- I COULD DIE.

THE VOICE IN MY HEAD BEGINS TO CHANT.

I COULD DIE.

THE NEXT MORNING.

WAKE UP.

HMM?

LET'S *GO!*

TESSA...?

I'M NOT SLEEPING...

...I'M ONNA STAKEOUT.

THAT'S LOVE'S HOTEL OVER THERE.

I *KNOW.* SHE PHONED THE CAPTAIN WHEN SHE SAW YOU ON THE BENCH THIS MORNING.

SHE *SAYS* YOU FOLLOWED HER LIMO WITH YOUR SCOOTER AFTER UPENDING A SHELF FULL OF *BRICKS* ON HER.

SHE'S LYING. IT WAS A SHELF FULL OF CLEANING FLUIDS.

SHE *ALSO* SAID SHE THINKS THE DEATH THREATS HAVE BEEN COMING FROM *YOU!* YOU'RE CREEPING ME OUT, BOBBY.

I SAW THE GUITAR YOU HAD BEFORE. ADMIT IT, YOU'RE OBSESSED WITH ALLANAH LOVE.

WHAT?!?

I USED TO BE CRAZY FOR LEO DECAPRIO BUT I NEVER UPENDED ANYTHING ON HIM.

LOOK, I TOLD TANNER I COULD HANDLE YOU, AND WE CAN KEEP THIS QUIET.

BUT *STAY* AWAY FROM THE SHOW TONIGHT. IT COULD MEAN YOUR BADGE.

THAT'S WHEN I FINALLY CAME UP WITH MY PLAN.

NOT A GOOD PLAN, MIND YOU. I THOUGHT OF IT IN UNDER A SECOND.

SLAM!

LOVE PITCHED IN AND STOPPED LANCE FROM IMPROVISING BEYOND THAT FIRST SHOT.

UHN! THE PAIN FROM THE BULLET WOUND WAS A FREIGHT TRAIN UP MY ARM-- BUT IT WAS ALL PART OF THE PLAN.

ONCE I'D SEEN DECOY IN THE ROOM--ALL I HAD TO DO WAS END UP THE MOST INJURED PERSON THERE.

SO A COUPLE OF DAYS LATER, I'D MANAGED TO CONVINCE EVERYBODY THAT I'D BEEN TO A HOSPITAL FOR MY SHOULDER, WHICH WAS ANOTHER LIE.

AND THE MAYOR PINNED THE MEDAL ON ME, CAREFUL TO AVOID THE WOUND THAT WASN'T THERE.

TANNER AND TESSA SAID THEY WERE PROUD OF ME.

ALLANAH LOVE TOLD ME I WAS THE BRAVEST MAN SHE EVER MET.

BUT I KNEW IN MY HEART THAT I TOOK THAT BULLET FOR PURELY SELFISH REASONS.

TO GET DECOY BACK.

AND IT WORKED.

I GOT EVERYTHING I WANTED.

BUT I DON'T THINK I GOT WHAT I NEEDED.

WHICH WAS-- TO LEARN MY LESSON.

AND TO LEARN TO TRUST MORE.

I START ON THAT TOMORROW.

THE END.

Better Angels

STORY: Phil Hester
PENCILS: Mitchell Breitweiser
INKS: James Taylor
COLORS: Mike Garcia
LETTERS: Ed Dukeshire

THE HELL? IS THAT A *COP?* TOO DARK TO TELL WITHOUT THE SPOT.

OF COURSE.

IT'S GOTTA BE LUCK.

DECOY, LISTEN TO ME VERY CAREFULLY.

NO MATTER WHAT HAPPENS, I WANT YOU TO STAY WITH THE GIRL. KEEP HER GOING.

EXACTLY WHO YOU TALKING TO, MAN?

YOU UNDERSTAND ME, D? STAY WITH *HER.* SHE'S YOUNG. SHE HAS A LOT OF LIFE AHEAD OF HER.

YOU'VE WON ME MORE THAN MY SHARE OF BORROWED TIME ALREADY.

HE'S LOST IT.

DECOY, I--I JUST WANT TO SAY... I DON'T KNOW... JUST...

...THANK YOU.

DECOY.

YOU SAVED MY LIFE AGAIN.

HARD... TO SPEAK WITH... THIS VOICE....

BUT YOU... MUST KNOW... YOU TEACH ME... SO MANY TIMES...

...TO HAVE... MERCY.

YOU SHOW ME... HOW TO BE... HUMANE.

YOU SAVE MY LIFE... EVERY... DAY.

UMM. HEY.

LUCK! HOW THE HELL DID YOU GET OUT OF THERE?

JUMPED DOWN TO THE FIRE ESCAPE. DIDN'T THINK I COULD WAIT WITH THE GIRL LIKE SHE IS.

End.

Big Top Decoy

Story: Scott Zirkel

Pencils & Inks: Ben Roman

Colors: Mike Garcia

Letters: Ed Dukeshire

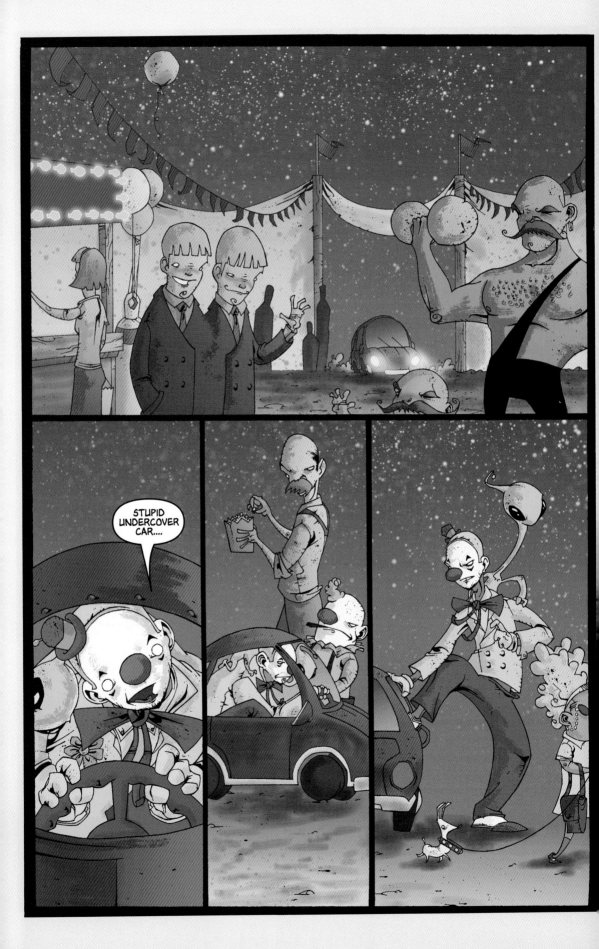

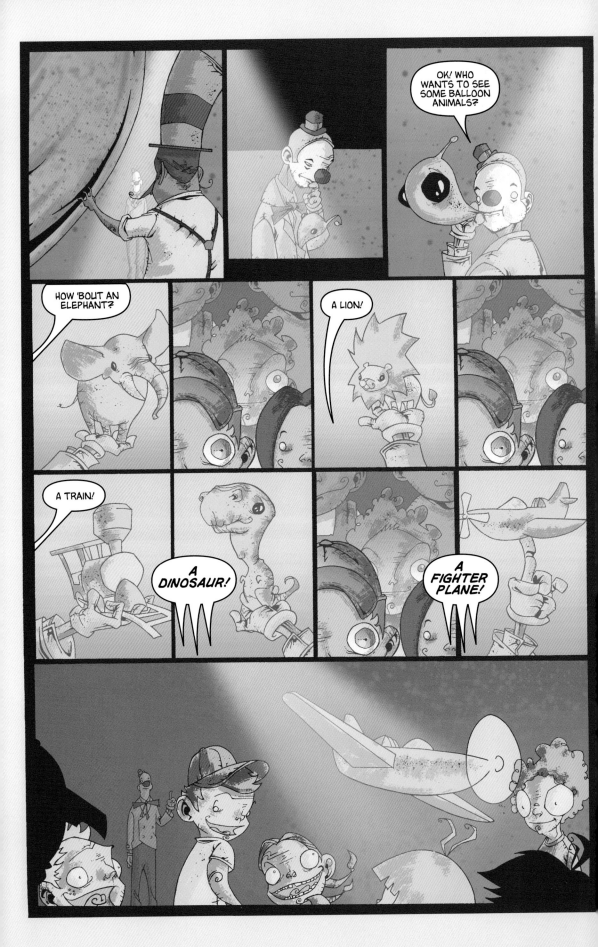

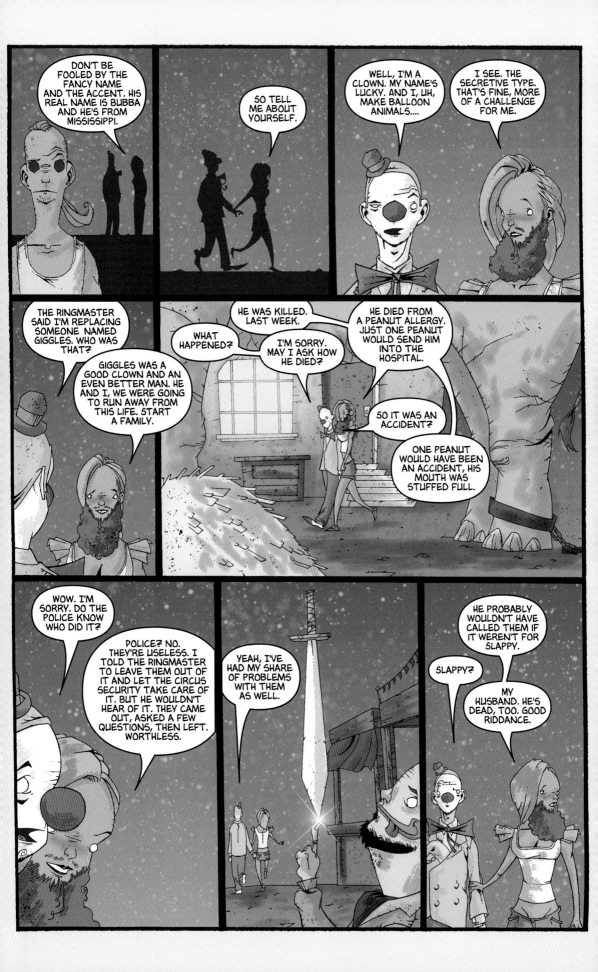

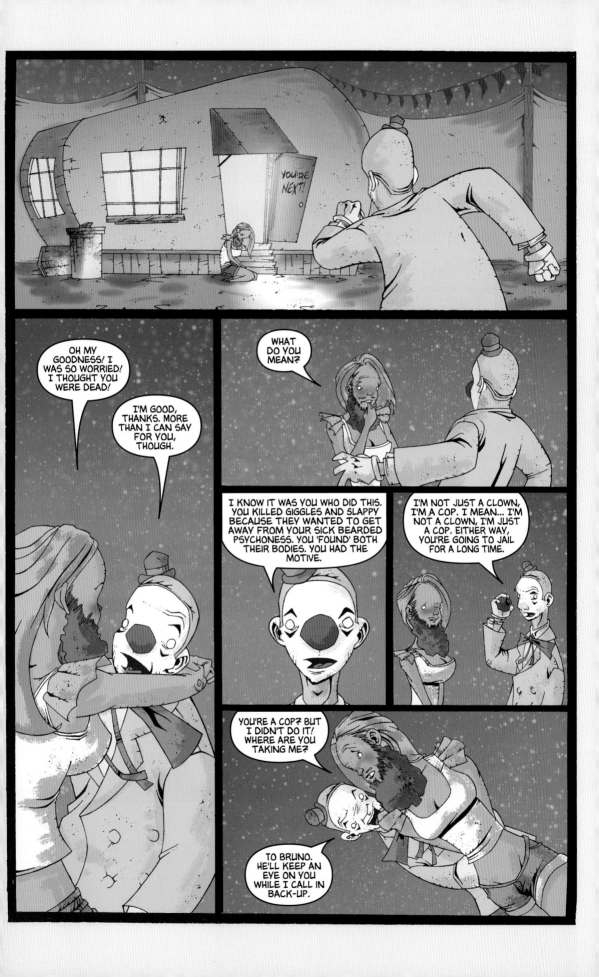

A Day in the Life

Story: Joshua Dysart
Pencils: Courtney Huddleston
Inks: James Taylor
Colors: Mike Garcia
Letters: Ed Dukeshire

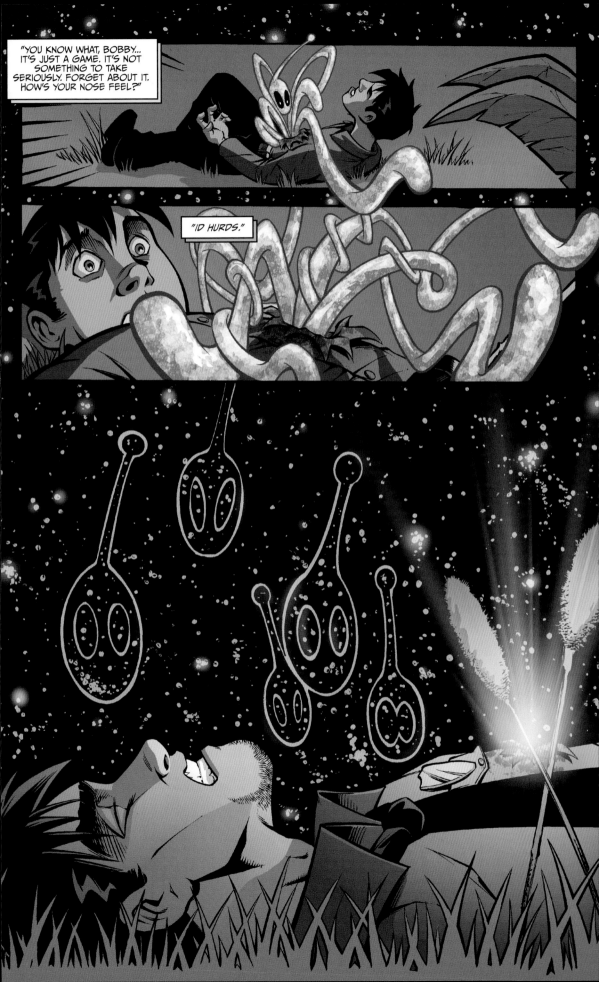

THE ALIEN GETS A GREAT SENSE OF PEACE FROM BEING BONDED TO LUCK. A SORT OF SETTLED LIGHTNESS.

IT'S A TESTAMENT TO JUST HOW GOOD A PERSON LUCK REALLY IS.

YOU KNOW, I NEVER USED TO CRAVE THIS WEIRD STUFF EITHER.

IT'S LIKE I'M PREGNANT OR SOMETHING.

I KNOW IT'S HOW YOU GET YOUR NUTRIENTS, BUT IT'S WEIRD FOOD, DECOY, THAT'S ALL I'M SAYING.

RIGHT ABOUT NOW THE FAIR MINDED READER MAY ASK, "HOW DID A SENSITIVE MAN LIKE LUCK BECOME A COP IN THE FIRST PLACE?"

LUCK'S FATHER AND GRANDFATHER WERE BOTH COPS... THAT'S PART OF IT.

HEY, POP IT, WILL YA?

BUT ALSO, LUCK ALWAYS ASSUMED THAT THIS WAS THE BEST WAY TO HELP PEOPLE.

ANYTHING BACK THERE?

'SUP?

MAYBE THINGS WERE DIFFERENT BACK IN HIS POP'S AND PAPAW'S RESPECTIVE DAYS.

MAYBE THAT'S NAÏVE. MAYBE THINGS HAVE ALWAYS BEEN THIS WAY. MAYBE THEY WERE JUST HARDER MEN.

OH... OH, GOD...

...IS... IS THAT THE LITTLE GIRL FROM...?

EITHER WAY, BOBBY LUCK OFTEN THINKS HE SHOULD'VE BECOME A FIREMAN INSTEAD.

ON THE RARE NIGHTS WHEN LUCK DOES SUCCUMB TO THE DARKNESS--WHEN HIS PSYCHE CAN NO LONGER HOLD BACK THE WELLING TIDE...

...THEN THE ALIEN DOES ALL HE CAN TO CALM EVERY IOTA OF LUCK'S BEING.

HE REACHES DOWN INTO LUCK'S UNCONSCIOUS AND ROOTS AROUND FOR A MEMORY... A MEMORY THAT WILL SOOTHE.

BONUS

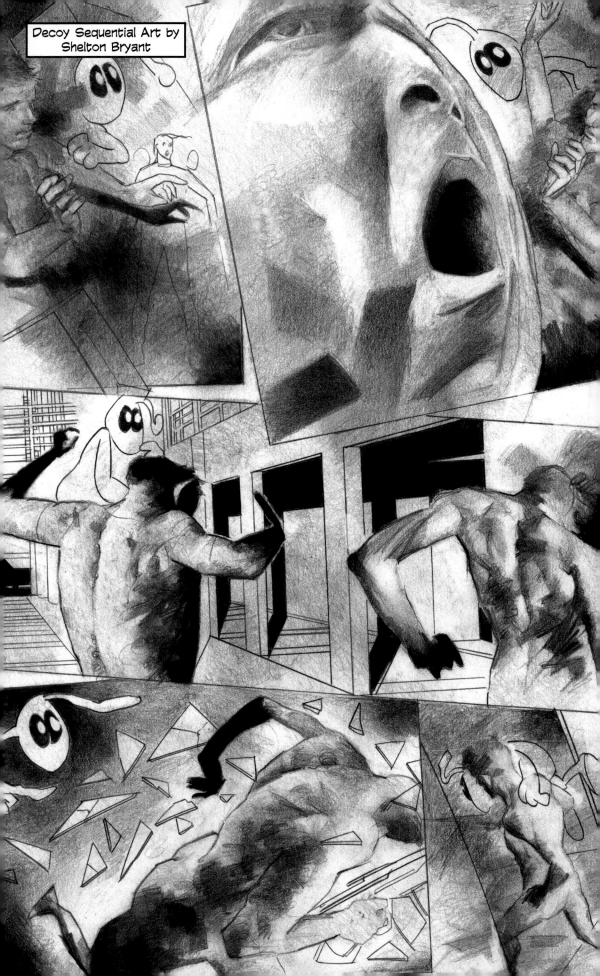

Decoy Sequential Art by
Shelton Bryant

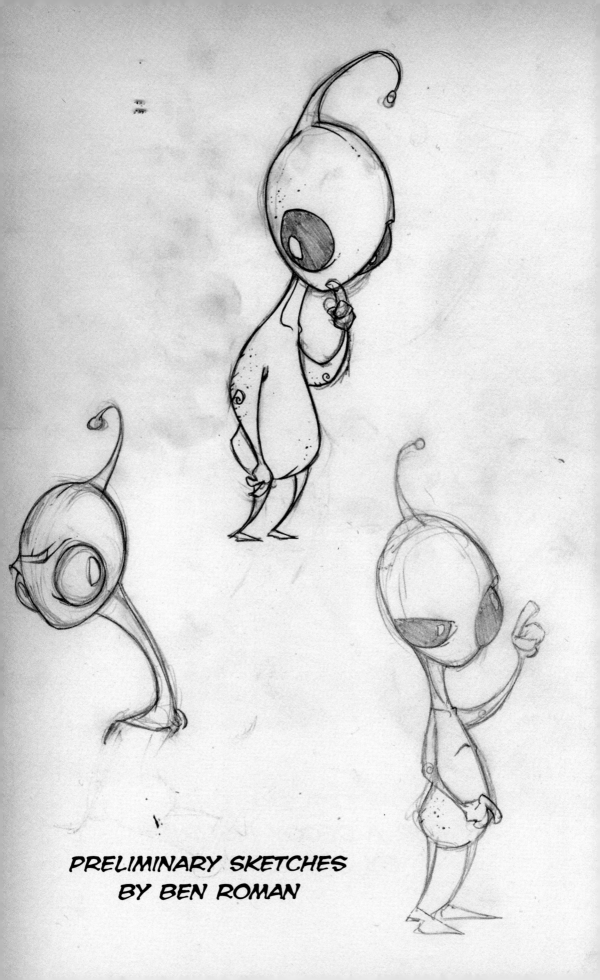

PRELIMINARY SKETCHES
BY BEN ROMAN

CONCEPT SKETCHES
FOR A DECOY FIGURINE
BY JOE CHIODO

ALTERNATE VIEW OF
CONCEPT SKETCHES
FOR DECOY FIGURINE

CONTRIBUTORS

Born in Guerrero Negro, Mexico, Fernando currently resides in Tijuana. He has always been passionate about drawing and working as a penciler, and has found many artists that have influenced his work in the comic-book industry. *Wizard* magazine's "How To Draw" section especially has taught Fernando a lot of techniques. He has also taken part in expositions at Tijuana's Cultural Center and has been published in local magazines and on websites.

In his own words: "Ahora gracias a Martin Montiel y a Courtney Huddleston de Penny-Farthing Press puedo ver impreso mi trabajo. Espero poder seguir en haciendo comics y que la industria cresca cada dia mas!"

MITCHELL BREITWEISER

Although Mitchell and his wife, Mindy, are Arkansas natives at heart, they currently live and work in New York City. Mitchell launched his career on Image's *Phantom Jack*, and was able to make a small name for himself with his cinematic storytelling and unique art style. Mitchell is now on board with Marvel Comics, working on a project that should be out in the fall of 2005. More information on Mitchell can be found at his website, www.mitchellillustration.com.

ED DUKESHIRE

In 1997, Ed Dukeshire created www.digitalwebbing.com, a website devoted to helping talent meet and create projects for the comics industry. It is one of the most popular comics-related websites where comics fans visit to get the latest news.

Ed founded the DW imprint in 2001 and began publishing *Digital Webbing Presents*, a collaborative anthology written and drawn by aspiring comics professionals who met on the Digital Webbing website. Since that time, the line has grown to include the work of several independent comics creators.

Ed began lettering stories in DWP and now finds himself in high demand to assist other publishers with his unique lettering style.

JOSHUA DYSART

Joshua Dysart co-created and wrote the cult-hit comic-book series *Violent Messiahs* for Image Comics. The first eight issues of which are collected in the graphic novel, *Violent Messiahs, Volume I: Book of Job.*

More recently his comics projects have included the DC six-issue mini-series *The Demon: Driven Out*, the Dark Horse one-shot *Van Helsing: Beneath the Rue Morgue,* and PFP's *Captain Gravity and The Power of the Vril.* He's currently the monthly writer on Vertigo's *Swamp Thing.*

He lives by the beach. He loves his mother. He's trying to learn how to hold himself in the palm of his own hand, but has yet to figure it out. I think he's afraid, and that's what's holding him back. He really digs writing for a living. He recommends it over almost all other forms of slavery.

SEAN GALLOWAY

Sean "Cheeks" Galloway was born in Little Rock, Arkansas, in 1974. He is a self-taught artist whose published work includes: *Venom #13*, *Wildguard: Fire Power, El Zombo, Decoy*, and *Teen Titans Go* covers. He has also done character development and storyboarding for Sony Entertainment.

He is currently based in San Diego, California.

MIKE GARCIA

APB: The colorist formerly know as Mike Garcia, now going under the alias The Big Peanutt or just a symbol of a nut, is said to be hiding out in gloomy, Southern California. This salty hooligan is so brash, one "T" just wasn't enough. With Mrs. Nutt and The Little Peanutt by his side, The Big Peanutt sets out to destroy all comics art that crosses his path. This Nutt is said to be "un" armed but dangerous. We have three of his powder-puffed cronies, J.T-Bone Steak, Stinky-Cheese Huddlestoned, and Raunchy Jam Woody in custody, but we need your help to find the Big Guy. Beneath his ridiculous shell hides a nuttcase who takes himself much too seriously.

We believe The Big Peanutt is devising a plot for creative world domination as we speak and could be hidden in plain sight. Several people, animals, and…things including elephants, baseball park vendors, and angry artists will not rest until he is caught.

PHIL HESTER

Phil Hester lives in rural Iowa with his wife and two children. He began working in comics while attending The University of Iowa. He graduated with a BFA in drawing with minors in sculpture and painting. He has worked for nearly every comic-book publisher in the last nineteen years and his work has been featured in over 300 published comics.

Phil's past works includes: *Swamp Thing, Detective, The Crow: Waking Nightmares, The Coffin* (writer), *The Wretch* ('96 Eisner Nominee), *The Creeper, Ultimate Marvel Team-Up, Brave Old World, Fringe, Rust, Namor, Taboo, The Picture Taker* (writer), *Attitude Lad, Deadline USA, Negative Burn, Clerks: The Lost Scene* and lots, lots more. His current and upcoming works are as follows: *Green Arrow, Deep Sleeper,* and *Firebreather: The Iron Saint*.

He is nice and likes nice people.

AZAD INJEJIKIAN

According to official North Korean accounts, Azad was born in a log cabin at his father's guerrilla base on North Korea's highest mountain, Mount Paektu, in February 1942. The peak, on the northern border with Chinese Manchuria, is the highest on the peninsula and the site where Korean legend says the nation came into existence 5,000 years ago. The event was reportedly marked by a double rainbow and a bright star in the sky.

Western researchers, however, believe that Azad was actually born and raised in Montreal, from where he wrote and drew the mini-series *Sammy: Tourist Trap* and the one-shot *A Very Sammy Day* (both from Image Comics). Recently, he has begun updating an online comics serial called *Subway Stories* on his website, which is projected to run until 2006. He is occasionally spotted in the industry doing pinups, covers, and nude modeling.

His current whereabouts are not known. He is considered armed, but harmless.

www.guerrilla-comics.com

ARVID NELSON

Arvid is a shy, intellectual SWM whose hobbies include Muppet impersonations, Japanese robots, proselytizing for Apple Computer, and radical leftist wankery. He writes a title through Image Comics called *Rex Mundi*. *Rex Mundi* is, according to Arvid's mother, a "work of genius that everyone should read." She assures Arvid "she would feel that way even if she weren't his mother," so go buy the first trade paperback, which is out now.

BEN ROMAN

All but giving up on breaking into the biz, Benjamin took a job at a Los Angeles Kinko's where he met a Tokyo Pop employee. He liked Benjamin's stuff and showed it to his editor. Benjamin is now working on his own book, *I Luv Halloween*, due out later this year. Benjamin owns a mini-fridge and hopes to save enough money to buy a real refrigerator. Time will tell.

ROVE

In 1981, Rove was born in the far north in a land called Canada. Not much is known about this "Canada" or this "1981", but Rove seems to think there is. He believes that "Canada" is the name of the country he is from, and "1981" is the year he was born.

I guess we'll just have to take his word for it.

Rove works doing design/illustration work in his homeland and attributes his love for comics to his 1980s childhood. Will he ever succeed in making a comic book? I guess we'll never truly know...but we can only hope that the answer to that question is no.

JAMES TAYLOR

James Taylor has a background in traditional art and received a BFA (Fine Arts Degree) with an emphasis in graphic design in 1998. After finishing college he began work as a graphic designer in the tech industry until 2002, surviving the bursting tech bubble by a couple of years. It was during his time as a designer that James started working in the comic-book industry in 1999. He started as a moonlight inker, thinking that the gig would just be a fun, side job, but switched to full-time comics work when his employer closed up shop. Since then, James has worked for many different publishers but seems to have been strapped to the hip of PFP over the last two years working on *The Victorian, Stuart Moore's Para* and, of course, *Decoy*.

James currently resides in the Seattle area, continually working as a freelance inker and graphic designer, and is rarely allowed to leave his home. In 2003, he started his own little publishing company, Rorschach Entertainment, to give new creators an opportunity to work in the comic-book industry–quite often publishing many creators' first work.

TY TEMPLETON

Ty was born in the wilds of downtown Canada to show business Gypsies. His father had more to do with the birth of televangelism than anyone in the family would care to admit, but that is mitigated by the fact that at least one newspaper accused Ty's father of being responsible for the death of Elvis. (You can look both these fun facts up on the internet. They're true!)

Ty has spent a misspent youth, and now the start of a misspent middle age toiling in the comics industry for such companies as Eclipse, DC, Marvel, BONGO, and now Penny-Farthing Press, working on *Batman, The Simpsons, Ren & Stimpy, Justice League, Superman, The Avengers, Elongated Man*, and lots, lots more.

He lives in the wilds of suburban Canada with four kids, one wife, three cats, uncounted fish, and more cartoons on video tape than is safe for any one man.

RYAN WOODWARD

Ryan Woodward, raised by a family of Quakers, grew up in downtown Los Angeles. As a child, he was beaten grotesquely by gangs of buff, wide-shouldered men who always wore their hats backwards. The Quakers, embarrassed by his inability to defend himself, abandoned him. A Mexican took pity on him and then took him in, but communication was hard. Both spoke English, but for some reason they could not understand one another. So they drew pictures in order to have conversations. Ryan stayed with the Mexican because the Mexican wore cool shirts and Ryan wanted them for himself.

Since then, his art exhibits hidden messages of violence and Mexican food. One day he vows to exterminate anyone in the comic-book industry who has biceps thicker than his thighs. Ryan resides peaceably in Utah, living in an old WW2 tank.

SCOTT ZIRKEL

Scott Zirkel has been working for many years as Courtney Huddleston's personal bodyguard. After working for him for so long, Scott realized that not only was Court not in any danger, but nobody even knew who he was. Scott read a few of Court's books and thought to himself, "If he can get paid for this, why can't I?" He soon entered the glamorous world of writing. Scott